On his k
a little p

It kept h

It shaded him from the sun.

It was perfect to take on holiday.

Sticky fancied a holiday in Pens' town. When he got there, he went to the beach.

'Time for a swim in the sea,' he said to himself. 'I'll leave my shelter on the sand.'

But when Sticky got out of the water, his shelter had gone.

'Oh, no!' he groaned.

'What's wrong?' asked Max.

'My shelter's gone,' wailed Sticky.

'Don't worry,' said Max. 'Pens will help you find it.'

 God will always help us if trouble comes – just as Pens help Sticky.

When someone helps us, what must we remember to say to them?

Pens Prayer

Father God, thank You that whatever happens, You're there beside me. Amen.

5

If Trouble Comes ...

'Trust in God at all times ... Tell him all your troubles ...'
(Psalm 62 v 8)

The shelter hunt

Sharpy

6

Introducing Pens

Gloria Glitter-pen

She's fabulously fashionable and adores hats. A bit of a fusspot maybe, but still there for a friend in need.

Charlotte Chalk

Cheerful and chirpy, she loves to sing! She's always happy to join in the fun whatever the day brings.

Denzil the Pencil

He's definitely the King of Cool, although perhaps not always as confident as he likes to make out.

Sharpy

He's lively, he's loveable, he knows how to get himself in a mess – and he's Pens' very best friend.

Splodge, I belong!

Well, Squiggle, I be short!

He he!

Pens

Helping you to get to know God more

Belonging to God

Written by

Alexa Tewkesbury

Every day a short Bible reading is brought to life with the help of the Pens characters. A related question and prayer apply this to daily life. Written in four sections, two focusing on the lives of Pens and two on Bible characters, young children will be inspired to learn more of God and His Word.

What's inside?

CWR

Day 1

IF TROUBLE COMES ...

'God is ... always ready to help in times of trouble.'
(Psalm 46 v 1)

Gone

4

Pens hunted everywhere for Sticky's lost shelter.

Max and Sharpy looked along one end of the beach. Denzil and Charlotte looked along the other.

Philippa and Gloria searched around the shops across the road. Marco, Squiggle and Splodge hunted in the park.

But they couldn't find Sticky's lost shelter anywhere.

Sticky sighed gloomily.

'It's gone forever,' he mumbled.

'No, it hasn't, Sticky,' said Philippa cheerfully. 'We promise we'll keep looking. We won't stop until we find it.'

 Whatever the problem, God never stops caring.

Do you ever feel like giving up when something is difficult? Ask God to help you keep trying.

Pens Prayer

Lord God, Your love for me goes on and on. I want my love for You to go on and on, too. Amen.

Day 3

If Trouble Comes ...

'... [God] is my strong protector; he is my shelter.'
(Psalm 62 v 7)

tick

tock

Denzil, the friend

Sticky looked at the time on the Pens' town clock.

'It's getting late,' he muttered.

Tick tock, tick tock.

'It's getting dark, too,' he frowned. 'We'll have to stop searching soon.'

'Never mind,' said Charlotte. 'We can carry on in the morning.'

'But what am I going to do?' Sticky worried. 'I was going to sleep under my shelter. Now it's lost, I've got nowhere to go.'

Denzil smiled kindly. 'Of course you have,' he said. 'You can stay at my house. You'll be warm and comfy, and I'll make something really tasty for supper.'

God hears us when we call to Him for help.

What's your favourite supper?

Pens Prayer

Dear Lord, if I know someone needs me, please help me to be a friend to them. Amen.

9

If Trouble Comes ...

'Turn to me, LORD ... save me from all my troubles.'
(Psalm 25 vv 16–17)

No sleep

Sticky ate a tasty supper with Denzil.

He was warm and comfy in Denzil's house.

But, when it was time for bed, Sticky couldn't get to sleep.

'Where's my shelter?'
he kept wondering.

He got up and shuffled about
in the bedroom.

'Where can it be?' he muttered.

He went downstairs and shuffled
about in the kitchen.

'Supposing I never find it?'
he worried.

All Sticky's shuffling and worrying
woke Denzil.

'Sticky,' Denzil yawned, 'we're
supposed to be sleeping.'

'Can't,' Sticky mumbled.
'Can't stop worrying.'

'I'll make us some hot chocolate,'
said Denzil. 'We can sit up together.'

 God doesn't want us to
worry about things – but He
understands when we do.

What's the last thing you do before you go to sleep?

Pens Prayer

Father God, when I'm
worried, please help me
remember that You are
looking after me. Amen.

Hello!

Denzil yawned.

He had been awake with Sticky nearly all night long.

'You look *really* sleepy,' frowned Max.

'I *am* really sleepy,' said Denzil. 'Sticky's been up all night worrying, and I stayed up with him.'

'Go to bed now, then,' replied Marco kindly. 'Sticky can have breakfast with us.'

'Thank you!' smiled Denzil. 'I need some sleep so I can carry on helping with the shelter hunt.'

If trouble comes, God likes us to help each other.

Who usually gets up first in the morning in your house?

Pens Prayer

Lord, thank You for being with me all through the day and all through the night. Amen.

13

Day 6 If Trouble Comes ...

'Be patient and wait for the LORD to act ...'
(Psalm 37 v 7)

Pens' Promise

Max and Marco made a big breakfast for Sticky.

'Thank you,' said Sticky. 'But I need to go and look for my shelter.'

'When you're busy,' replied Max, 'it's very important to eat a proper breakfast.'

'That's right,' agreed Marco. 'You won't be able to do any shelter-hunting if you're hungry.'

Sticky nibbled a piece of toast.

'Can we start looking soon?' he asked.

'Of course,' smiled Max. 'And anyway, Philippa and Charlotte had their breakfast early. So they're out looking already.'

'Just to help *me*?' asked Sticky.

Marco nodded. 'Because we promised,' he said.

When we need Him, God won't leave us on our own.

What's your favourite breakfast?

Pens Prayer

Thank You, Lord, for all the people who love me and help me. Amen.

15

If Trouble Comes ...

'I am always aware of the LORD'S presence; he is near, and nothing can shake me.' (Psalm 16 v 8)

Denzil's good idea

Pens sat on the beach. Sticky sat with them.

They'd searched for Sticky's shelter from one end of Pens' town to the other.
They couldn't find it anywhere.

We must be looking in the wrong places.

Sticky said nothing.

Suddenly, Denzil cried, 'I know what to do!'

'Do you know where to look?' Sticky asked.

'No,' Denzil answered. 'But it doesn't matter. If we can't find your old shelter, we'll help you build a brand-new one.'

Sticky blinked.

Sticky smiled.

That was the best idea he'd heard all day.

But there aren't many places left.

Our Father God can give us good ideas when we ask Him to help us!

What good ideas have you had this week?

Pens Prayer

Lord God, thank You for encouraging me with good ideas. Help me to encourage other people, too. Amen.

17

Day 8

If Trouble Comes ...

'Hear me, LORD, when I call to you!' (Psalm 27 v 7)

A prayer for Sticky

18

Pens were having one last hunt around Pens' town for Sticky's shelter.

'It must be here somewhere,' said Gloria. 'Perhaps we should ask someone else to help us.'

'Yes,' Philippa nodded. 'Let's ask God.'

Pens sat down, with Sticky beside them, and they prayed.

They thanked God that Sticky had come to Pens' town for his holiday.

They told Him how sad Sticky was without his special shelter.

They asked Him to be with them as they helped Sticky to search for it.

Then they set off again, knowing God was beside them.

Suddenly …

'Look!' squealed Splodge.

Our Father God loves to be with us – on good days, bad days, always.

Are you doing anything special this week? Ask God to go with you.

Pens Prayer

Loving Lord, whatever I'm doing, I'm so happy that You're beside me. Amen.

Day 9   If Trouble Comes ...

'Praise the LORD ... Praise him now and for ever! Amen! Amen!' (Psalm 41 v 13)

At last!

20

Splodge was looking over Miss Fountain Pen's garden gate. Pens and Sticky looked, too.

Under a tree was Miss Fountain Pen.

She was sitting at a round garden table.

The tabletop was made of … Sticky's shelter!

'My shelter!' shrieked Sticky.

'Your what?' asked Miss Fountain Pen.

When Pens explained, Miss Fountain Pen was very sorry.

'I found it on the beach,' she said. 'I didn't think anyone wanted it.'

'That's all right,' smiled Sticky. 'I'm just SO happy to see it again. Thank you for helping me, Pens,' he added. 'You're the best friends ever.'

 If trouble comes, remember that God will never let us down.

Do you have a garden? Is there any special garden furniture in it?

Pens Prayer
Father God, You've promised that I can trust You every day and everywhere. Praise You! Amen.

THE PATH THROUGH THE SEA
God rescues His people

Day 10

'I am the LORD; I will rescue you and set you free ...' (Exodus 6 v 6)

The Bad King of Egypt

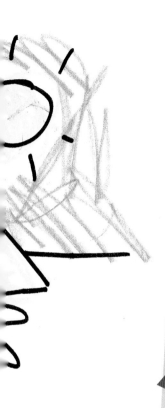

The king of Egypt was a bad man.

He was unkind to God's special friends, the Israelites.

He made them work for him for no money.

He wouldn't let them leave his country.

This made God angry. *So* angry that He made life very hard for the king and for all the people in Egypt.

At last the king of Egypt said, 'I've had enough of this!'

He sent for a man called Moses. Moses was the leader of God's people.

'Get out!' the king shouted at him. 'Get out of Egypt and take all the Israelites with you!'

 God's people were in trouble but He had a plan to rescue them.

How would God's people have felt when the king let them go?

Pens Prayer

Dear Lord, thank You that You are my Daddy in heaven who loves me. Amen.

The Path Through The Sea
God rescues His people

Day 11

'What have we done? We ... have lost [the Israelites] as our slaves!' (Exodus 14 v 5)

'After them!'

When the king told God's people to go, Moses hurried them out of Egypt.

God told Moses to take them towards the Red Sea. Then He stayed close to them to lead them all the way there.

But suddenly, the king changed his mind!

'I don't want the Israelites to leave!' he shouted. 'Who will do all the work? I need my slaves back.'

The king's army got themselves ready.

The king himself jumped into his war chariot.

'Let's bring those Israelites back!' the king ordered.

And they all set out after God's people.

 God's people would have to trust Him to help them escape.

Who do you think was stronger – the king and his army, or God?

Pens Prayer

Father God, when I have a bad day or a sad day, I want to keep trusting You. Amen.

Day 12

'When the Israelites saw the king and his army ... they ... cried out to the LORD for help.' (Exodus 14 v 10)

Behind you!

'What's that coming behind us?' God's people wondered.

At once, they realised.

It wasn't something good.

It was something very bad.

The king and his army!

'What are we going to do?' God's people cried.

They were terrified.

In front of them was the Red Sea.

It was deep and dark and very, very wide.

Moses had led them there because God had told him to. But however were they going to get across?

'Why have you brought us here, Moses?' God's people screamed. 'Please, Lord God, please help us!'

 Moses trusted God, but God's people were very frightened.

Do you ever play chasing games at school or preschool?

Pens Prayer

Dear Lord God, You've promised to be with me always. Thank You. Amen.

The Path Through The Sea
God rescues His people

Day 13

'Don't be afraid! … The LORD will fight for you … '
(Exodus 14 vv 13–14)

The wonderful Path

28

Moses knew God would never give His people back to the bad king of Egypt.

He was sure God had a plan to save them.

'Don't be scared!' he called out to the Israelites. 'God has promised to rescue us, and that's what He will do.'

'Moses,' God said. 'Lift up your walking stick and hold it over the sea.'

Moses did as God said.

God's people stood watching.

First, the wind began to blow. Then all the people gasped.

A sandy path was opening up – right through the middle of the sea!

The sea was a problem for God's people, but it wasn't a problem for God!

When there's no 'wonderful path', how do people usually travel across the sea?

Pens Prayer

Father God, thank You that when I have a problem, You have the answer. Amen.

'… the Israelites walked through the sea on dry ground …' (Exodus 14 v 29)

Escape through the sea

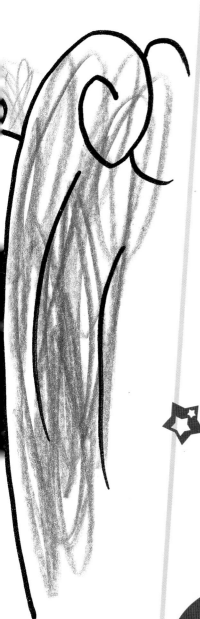

Moses put one foot on the path through the sea. The ground was firm and dry.

'Come on!' he called to God's people. 'Follow me!'

So God's people hurried after Moses.

They crossed the Red Sea on God's path.

They walked all the way to the other side.

They didn't even get their feet wet!

But, behind them, something bad was happening.

God's people pointed.

'Look!' they shouted.

The king of Egypt and his army were crossing the sea on the path, too!

 God's people were still in trouble, but He knew how to keep them safe.

How can you keep your feet dry in wet weather?

Pens Prayer
Lord God, You never stop caring for me. Praise You! Amen.

The Path Through The Sea
God rescues His people

Day 15

'... they had faith in the LORD and in his servant Moses.' (Exodus 14 v 31)

Safe at last

32

The king of Egypt and his army were getting closer.

As soon as God's people were safely on the other side of the Red Sea, God ordered, 'Moses! Hold your stick out over the water again.'

Moses did as God said.

God's people stood watching.

This time, the sea came crashing back down.

All over God's path.

All over the king and his army.

Every one of them was washed away.

'We're safe!' God's people cried. 'We're out of Egypt!'

Then they praised God. At last they'd learnt to trust Him.

God showed His people that He would NEVER let them down.

God made a wonderful path through the sea. What do people build to get across rivers?

Pens Prayer

Father God, Your love for me is stronger than all the waves in the sea! Thank You! Amen.

Day 16

GOD AND ME

'You believed in Christ, and God put his stamp of ownership on you ...' (Ephesians 1 v 13)

'Sharpy is my best friend,' said Max to Denzil one day.

'He plays football with me.

'He goes to the park with me.

'He runs on the beach with me.

'I can talk to him when I'm happy. I can talk to him when I'm sad.

'Sharpy will always be "MY Sharpy". What can I give him as a very special present?'

Denzil looked thoughtful. Then, 'What about a tag for his collar?' he suggested. 'A tag that says: "I belong to Max"?'

'Brilliant!' beamed Max. 'Then Sharpy will know we're together forever.'

Sharpy belongs to Max just as Jesus' friends belong to God.

What needs to be written on your books or pictures so that your teacher knows who they belong to?

Pens Prayer

Thank You, dear Lord, that You don't just know my name, You know everything about me. I love belonging to You! Amen.

God and Me

'… with all your heart do what God wants …'
(Ephesians 6 v 6)

'my max'

'Max is my best friend,' thought Sharpy to himself one day. 'I'm so glad we belong together.'

Sharpy always tried hard to do as Max asked him to.

He was ready to go out when Max went for a walk.

He was ready to play when Max picked up his football.

He was very excited to see Max when he came home from school.

Sometimes, Sharpy did things wrong, but he was always sorry afterwards.

Sharpy loved Max so much, he just wanted to make him happy.

 When we belong to God, we should try to live the way He asks us to.

How can you show the people you love that they're special to you?

Pens Prayer

Father God, You are so special to me. Thank You that I'm special to You, too. Amen.

37

God and Me

'God … has created us for a life of good deeds …'
(Ephesians 2 v 10)

Pens' town Park

It was a stormy night in Pens' town. In the morning, Squiggle and Splodge went to the park.

'What a mess!' said Squiggle.

The wind had blown all the litter bins over. There was rubbish everywhere.

'Oh dear,' frowned Splodge. 'Pens won't be able to enjoy the park while it looks like this.'

'Let's tidy it up,' said Squiggle.

When they'd finished, every bit of rubbish was back in the bins.

'Hello!' called a voice. It was Gloria. 'Doesn't the park look beautiful?' she said.

Squiggle and Splodge smiled.

'Yes,' they replied. 'It really does.'

God made us to be thoughtful and kind.

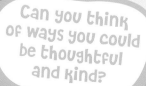

Can you think of ways you could be thoughtful and kind?

Pens Prayer

Lord God, please help me to be thoughtful in the things I do and kind to the people I meet. Amen.

Looks smart.

'Hello!' called Denzil.
'Do you like my new watch?'

'It looks brilliant,' Philippa said.

'Philippa!' called Max.
'Do you like my new football?'

'Wow!' Philippa said.

'Morning!' called Gloria.
'Do you like my new bag?'

'Very pretty,' Philippa said.

'Listen!' called Charlotte.
'Do you like my new song?'

'Lovely,' Philippa said.

Philippa spent so long with Pens, she couldn't finish her gardening.

'But they were all very excited,' she thought. 'God would want me to spend time with them.'

 Philippa belongs to God, so she wants to make Him happy.

How would Pens feel if Philippa said she didn't have time to talk to them?

Pens Prayer

Dear Lord, I'm so happy to belong to You. Please help me to make You happy, too. Amen.

Charlotte looked out of her window. The sky was blue.

Gloria picked some flowers for her kitchen. Their colours were bright.

Denzil was on the beach. The sand was golden.

Philippa went into her garden. The sun was shining.

Max and Sharpy were in the park. The trees were beautiful.

Marco went for a paddle in the sea. The water was sparkling.

'I'm so happy we belong to God,' smiled Charlotte. 'He's given us such a wonderful world, and He's promised to be with us forever.'

When we belong to God, His blessings will never end.

What different colours can you see outside your bedroom window?

Pens Prayer

Thank You, Father, that You love to give me wonderful things to enjoy. Amen.

43

Day 21

God and Me

'… Christ came and preached the Good News of peace to all …' (Ephesians 2 v 17)

All over the world

At school, Marco was learning about the world outside Pens' town.

There were big countries. There were small countries.

There were dry countries. There were wet countries.

There were tiny islands. There were huge oceans.

There were animals, there were birds. There were fish, there were insects.

And there were SO MANY people!

'Can God really know EVERYONE, all over the whole world?' Marco asked Philippa.

'Oh, yes,' said Philippa. 'He knows everyone and He loves everyone. More than anything, God wants everyone to know who He is so that He can be their Friend.'

 Whoever we are, wherever we live, God wants us all to belong to Him.

Have you ever been to another country? Where have you visited in your own country?

Pens Prayer

Dear Lord, even though the world is so HUGE, You love everyone in it. Praise You! Amen.

God and Me

'… you must put on the new self, which is created in God's likeness …' (Ephesians 4 v 24)

Dressing UP

Charlotte and Gloria were having a dressing-up day.

They took all Gloria's pretty dresses out of her cupboard.

They took all her beautiful hats off the shelves.

Then they got dressed up in lots of different outfits.

'This is my "going shopping" outfit,' said Gloria.

'This could be my "going to the library" outfit,' laughed Charlotte.

'What about this for my "going on holiday" outfit?' asked Gloria.

'I like this for a "going out visiting" outfit,' smiled Charlotte.

Charlotte looked at herself in Gloria's mirror.

'Wow!' she beamed. 'Now that I'm dressed in your clothes, Gloria, I look just like you!'

 The closer we stay to God, the more like Him we will become.

Do you have a dressing-up box at home or at school? What would you like to dress up as?

Pens Prayer

Father God, when people look at me, please help them to see that I belong to You. Amen.

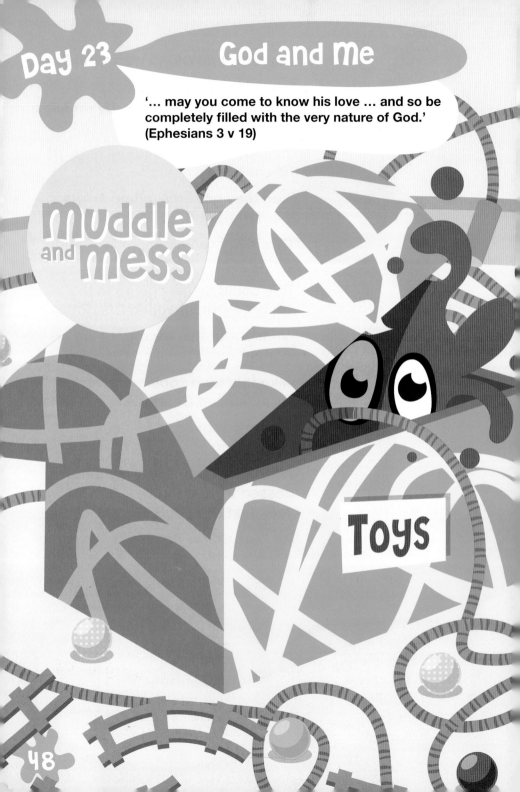

Splodge's bedroom was a muddle.

'I'll tidy it up,' smiled Squiggle to herself. 'Splodge will be so pleased. God likes us to make each other happy.'

'My bedroom looks beautiful!' cried Splodge. 'You're so kind, Squiggle. Thank you.'

Squiggle's toy box was a mess.

'I'll sort it out,' smiled Splodge to herself. 'Squiggle will be so pleased. God likes us to make each other happy.'

'My toy box looks brilliant!' cried Squiggle. 'You're so kind, Splodge. Thank you.'

Squiggle and Splodge knew how much God loved them. They wanted to share that love with each other.

 God's love for us helps us show love to those around us.

How could you show God's love to someone?

Pens Prayer

Lord God, thank You so much that I belong to You and You love me. Please help me to show Your love to other people. Amen.

49

Day 24

God and Me

'Even before the world was made, God had already chosen us to be his ....' (Ephesians 1 v 4)

Which goldfish?

50

Denzil was on his way to the pet shop to buy a goldfish.

'I've always wanted a goldfish of my very own,' he said.

He'd already bought a fish tank.

He'd put in little stones and special plants.

He'd filled the tank with water.

But when Denzil got to the pet shop, there wasn't just *one* goldfish for sale.

There were lots and lots.

He watched them swimming this way and that, fins flapping, tails flipping.

'There are so many, I don't know which one to choose,' he puzzled. 'I wish I had room for all of them.'

Denzil's tank wasn't big enough for all the goldfish. But God's heart is HUGE – big enough for everyone.

What other pets can you buy in a pet shop?

Pens Prayer

Loving Lord, thank You for choosing ME to belong to You! Amen.

51

Day 25

God and Me

'May God the Father and the Lord Jesus Christ give to all Christian brothers and sisters peace and love with faith.' (Ephesians 6 v 23)

A Postcard from Sticky

Something dropped onto Denzil's doormat.

Word up

52

It was a postcard from Sticky:

Dear Denzil,

Thank you very much for helping me when I lost my shelter. All you Pens were so kind.

I know God is YOUR special Friend, so I've been talking to Him. I've asked Him to be my special Friend – and now I belong to God, too!

See you soon.

Lots of love

Sticky

Denzil was so excited, he ran to tell Pens Sticky's good news.

'Now Sticky's one of God's family!' he beamed. 'Just like us!'

Because Pens showed Sticky God's love, he wanted to belong to God's family, too.

When do people usually send each other postcards?

Pens Prayer

Father God, YOUR good news is that You love me and forgive me when I do something wrong. MY good news is that I belong to You! Amen.

53

BELIEVE AND SEE

Jesus heals a man who is blind

Day 26

'Jesus of Nazareth is passing by ...' (Luke 18 v 37)

Jesus goes to Jericho

54

Jesus was walking to a town called Jericho.

'Jesus is coming to visit!' people told each other. 'Let's go and meet Him!'

Very soon, there were crowds in the streets. There were crowds along the roads.

One man sat beside the road all on his own.

He had no money.

Day after day he sat there, begging.

He could hear all the excitement. But he couldn't see anything because he was blind.

'What is it?' he called out. 'What's happening?'

'Jesus is coming!' people answered happily.

Wherever Jesus went, people were excited to see Him.

What good things has God given to you? Remember to say thank You to Him.

Pens Prayer

Jesus, I'm so excited that You are my Friend. Praise You! Amen.

Believe and See
Jesus heals a man who is blind

Day 27

'Jesus! … Take pity on me!' (Luke 18 v 38)

Trust

56

The man who couldn't see knew all about Jesus.

He knew that Jesus taught people about God.

He knew that Jesus made sick people well.

He knew that Jesus was very special.

'Jesus is coming here?' he thought. 'Then I must speak to Him. Jesus will help me, I know He will.'

The crowd was very noisy. The man knew he'd have to shout loudly if Jesus were going to hear Him.

'Jesus!' he called. 'Jesus, be kind to me, please!'

The man who was blind believed in Jesus completely.

What do you know about Jesus?

Pens Prayer

Dear Lord Jesus, please help me to trust You completely – just like the man who couldn't see. Amen.

Believe and See
Jesus heals a man who is blind

Day 28

'… Jesus stopped and ordered the blind man to be brought to him.' (Luke 18 v 40)

The man **shouts** louder

58

There were people waving to Jesus. There were people cheering Him.

But when they heard the man who couldn't see calling out, they were cross with him.

'Be quiet!' they said. 'Who do you think you are, shouting to Jesus like that?'

But the man wouldn't be quiet. Jesus was there and he had to speak to Him.

'Jesus!' he shouted again, even louder. 'Jesus, I need You! Please be kind to me.'

Jesus stopped. He looked at the man who had called to Him.

Then He said, 'Help that man up and bring Him over to Me.'

Jesus answers everyone who calls to Him.

Do you know someone who needs Jesus' help? Jesus listens when we ask Him to help others, too.

Pens Prayer

Dear Jesus, please help me remember to pray for other people as well as for myself. Amen.

Believe and See
Jesus heals a man who is blind

Day 29

'Your faith has made you well.' (Luke 18 v 42)

The miracle

Jesus stood in front of the man who was blind.

The man couldn't see His kind face. But he could hear His kind voice.

'Hello,' Jesus smiled. 'How can I help you? What is it you'd like Me to do?'

'Please, Sir,' the man began, 'I am blind and I want to be able to see.'

He waited for Jesus to answer.

The crowd of people nearby waited, too.

Jesus *did* answer.

'If you want to see, then you shall see,' He said. 'Because you trust Me so much, I will make your eyes better.'

Jesus could see how much the man believed in Him.

Have you ever asked Jesus to help you with something very important?

Pens Prayer

Thank You so much, Lord Jesus, that You love me and take care of me. Amen.

Believe and See
Jesus heals a man who is blind

Day 30

'… he followed Jesus, giving thanks to God.'
(Luke 18 v 43)

The man who could **see**

The man who was blind blinked.

Suddenly he could see the crowd of people around him.

Suddenly he could see Jesus' kind face.

The man wasn't blind any longer!

He started shouting again, louder than he'd ever shouted before.

'I can see!' he yelled. 'I can see! Thank You, Jesus! Thank You!'

The people watching were amazed and praised God, too.

And, as Jesus carried on walking to Jericho, the man who could see followed Him.

When we trust in Jesus, we can belong to God.

What sort of animal do we teach to help people who can't see to find their way around?

Pens Prayer

Dear Jesus, believing in You means God is my Friend and I am part of His big family, now and always. Praise You! Amen.

Pens for special times.

An exciting story plus daily Bible-reading notes

Easter

Help young children understand the true meaning of Easter.

Christmas

The *Pens* characters tell the Christmas story to make Jesus' birth real and memorable for young children.

Starting School

Help children start school confidently, knowing that God goes there with them.

Available online, or from Christian bookshops.

For current prices visit
www.cwr.org.uk/store